THE

JUMP START
LEADERSHIP WORKBOOK
IGNITE YOUR ABILITY TO LEAD & SUCCEED!

VOLUME 2:

LEADING OTHERS

BY
SCOTT GREENBERG

THE

JUMP START
LEADERSHIP WORKBOOK
IGNITE YOUR ABILITY TO LEAD & SUCCEED!

VOLUME 2:

LEADING OTHERS

BY

SCOTT GREENBERG

Cover Design, Illustrations and Layout By: Tony Francesconi
Edited By: Debi Klump

Printed in The United States of America

ISBN: 1-893962-01-6

For additional copies, call 1-800-450-0432.

Quantity discounts and class sets are available.

Consider selling these books at your next conference.

Contents

My Promise for the JUMP START Leadership Workbook Series

I promise...

By reading these workbooks, doing the exercises and applying the tools to your own life, you will enjoy more success than you can possibly imagine. Nothing in these workbooks is based on theory or classroom curriculum; it is all based on experience, observation, and most importantly, results.

For thousands of years great leaders have been using these methods (or versions of them) to accomplish their goals and create change. Nothing about these methods is complicated. Anyone, regardless of age, can apply these tools to his or her life and see results. The challenge is to believe in the methods enough to stick with them.

It is important to understand that success comes not just from what you do, but also from how you handle unexpected opportunities and challenges. And let's face it, you don't have complete control over all the things that affect your life. Stuff happens. And when it does, many people leave things up to chance and don't try to shape their own destiny. The truth is, you have more influence than you might think. These books will help you control of your life, influence others, and take advantage of all life has to offer.

No one in the world does everything suggested in this book. That would be superhuman. But accomplished people use some of these ideas. Your task is to try these techniques, adapt them to meet your own needs, and do what works best for you.

This volume, entitled LEADING OTHERS, is all about the skills you need to influence other people and lead them toward a common goal. After doing the reading and completing the exercises, you will enjoy an incredible amount of power. Use it wisely and responsibly.

Read the book. Do the exercises. Apply what you learn. If you do, you can become a successful leader.

I promise.

Scott Greenberg

INFLUENCING OTHERS
How to Earn And Keep People's Respect & Loyalty

"Serve them well and they will follow."

Having the power to influence others is not a talent but a privilege. We enjoy this privilege when others choose to follow us. The only way someone can lead is if others agree to comply with his or her wishes. There are various reasons why people might choose to follow someone else -- their job title, their age or even their physical strength. However, the most powerful leaders are those who can win the genuine love and respect of those around them. If you can do that, you can influence others.

In this chapter you will learn how to win people's loyalty and become the type of person they are honored to follow.

WHO INFLUENCES YOU?

To become an influential person, it's important to understand how *you* are influenced by others.

Answer the following questions:

1. Who are the people you most respect and admire (e.g., political leaders, business leaders, historical figures, teachers, athletes, rock stars, etc.)?

2. What specific qualities in them most impress you?

3. What makes these people different than other people?

If you can become aware of how you are influenced by leaders, you can use the same techniques they do to lead others. No need to reinvent the wheel when you can use the tools that already work.

©1999 Scott Greenberg

QUALITIES THAT WILL WIN YOU RESPECT

Honesty.

People appreciate being able to count on you for the truth.

Trust.

People will respect you if they know they can trust you – and if they feel you trust them.

Reliability.

No one likes a flake. Be someone others can count on to follow through on your commitments.

Honor.

Doing what is right isn't always easy. Perhaps that's why honorable people are given so much respect.

Integrity.

Be true to yourself and to what you believe in.

Kindness.

Treat others with care.

Confidence.

Believe in yourself. This is perhaps the most attractive quality of all.

Vision.

Give people an image of something to believe in.

A plan.

People respond to others who know how to make positive change.

Successfulness.

People notice how you behave and what you achieve.

Public speaking skills.

You must be able to communicate to motivate.

Listening skills.

People want to know they'll be heard.

Commitment.

What are you willing to do for others?

If people see these qualities in you, they will follow you to the end of the earth.

DELEGATING: GIVING "ORDERS"

Although people respect leaders, they don't always like being told what to do. No one likes to feel like they're in the military when they're not. Part of being an effective leader is getting people to do things with as much enthusiasm as you have in asking them. Here are some ways to motivate people to action:

Phrase your request respectfully.

Don't talk down to people or sound as if you are commanding them. Ask them as you would like to be asked.

Let people know why the task is necessary.

People like to be part of something important. Let them know how their contribution will make a difference for your cause.

Let them know why you've asked them.

Tell them why they are the best person for the job. They'll appreciate your faith in them.

Ask them how they think the task should be done.

Allow them to have input so they feel more personally involved.

Ask them if they have any questions.

Give them an opportunity to get any information they need.

Ask them what kind of help they'll need.

Let them know they're not alone.

Thank them in advance.

If you have time, offer assistance.

Show them you're willing to help do the work, rather than just assign it.

©1999 Scott Greenberg

GIVING FEEDBACK

Giving the people you lead feedback helps them perform better. It's important that you let them know what they're doing well, and how they can improve. Here are some tips for making the process as effective as possible.

Let them know in advance you'll be giving them feedback.

This way they won't be surprised by your comments and will be more open to what you have to say. Assure them you're offering feedback to help bring out the best in them.

Gather all the facts first.

Make sure you understand the entire situation before offering feedback. No one likes criticism from someone who doesn't know what's going on.

Comment on both good and bad behaviors.

People resent when you only notice or comment on their faults and not on what they are doing well. Positive reinforcement is just as important as constructive criticism.

Don't get personal.

Comment not on the person, but on what they are doing. Never name-call or criticize their personality.

Don't overdo it.

Don't comment on every situation. Over-criticizing can make the person bitter, and over-praising can make each compliment less significant. Focus on important behaviors that need attention.

Consider the time and place.

Avoid embarrassing the person or interrupting something important. Ask yourself when the feedback will be most productive for the person.

Choose your words carefully.

It doesn't take much to sound overly harsh. Your feedback should be clear without damaging the person's ego.

Keep it constructive and productive.

Make sure you have suggestions for improvement and not just criticism. Let them know you're interested in helping them succeed – not bringing them down.

Ask them what they think they need to do.

Solicit their ideas on how they can improve so they can take some responsibility for their performance.

©1999 Scott Greenberg

11

LEADING DIFFERENT PERSONALITIES

Not everyone you lead will have the same personality. People have different levels of skill, experience and confidence. Some will have fragile egos, while others will be overconfident. To bring out the best in your group, you will have to adapt your leadership style to suit each personality. Some people need a lot of feedback. Others deserve freedom and responsibility. Some require you to be more forceful. Think about each person you lead and ask yourself what kind of leadership style will bring out the best in them.

Let's practice. For the following people, act as if you were their leader. What kind of leadership style would be most appropriate? What kind of action should you take? Suggestions for each are on the following page:

1. Someone who's brand new and eager to learn.

2. Someone who's been around a while and has a bad attitude.

3. Someone who has a lot of experience and a great attitude.

4. Someone who has a little experience and is feeling discouraged.

5. Someone who refuses to do anything you ask them to do.

SUGGESTED ANSWERS

1. Someone who's brand new and eager to learn.

While they have a great attitude, they still probably don't know a lot about what they're supposed to do. Spend a lot of time training, helping and giving feedback. Don't let them do too much on their own until they've proven themselves.

2. Someone who's been around a while and has a bad attitude.

These types of people probably don't need too much training or reminders about what they are supposed to be doing. Perhaps they're just getting burnt out, or are feeling too confident and need a challenge. There may also be an outside issue you're not aware of. Ask questions. Don't order this type of person around too much. Address the problem, but show a great deal of respect and ask for their ideas for resolving the situation.

3. Someone who has a lot of experience and a great attitude.

These types of people just need to know what to do. Get their ideas on how things should be done. Don't get in their way too much. If they've proven themselves, let them do things their way. Give them a lot of freedom and let them know you're there if they need you.

4. Someone who has a little experience and is feeling discouraged.

They may be realizing the task is a little more difficult then they thought. Give them lots of encouragement and any help they may need. They may also be realizing they don't like what they're doing. Find out and work with them to improve their situation.

5. Someone who refuses to do anything you ask them to do.

This is unacceptable. Find out what the problem is and try to resolve it. Keep in mind it may be an outside issue. Let these types of people know why they are important to the group and why their cooperation is necessary. If they absolutely refuse to participate and you've made a reasonable effort to accommodate them, consider removing them from the group.

Make no mistake: The simple ideas you just read will make you a more powerful leader. Use these tools wisely and you will position yourself to influence large numbers of people to create major changes.

SUMMARY

- **Model yourself after those who influence you.**

- **Exhibit qualities that will win you respect.**

  - Honesty.

  - Trust.

  - Reliability.

  - Honor.

  - Integrity.

  - Kindness.

  - Confidence.

  - Vision.

  - A plan.

  - Successfulness.

  - Public speaking skills.

  - Listening skills.

  - Commitment.

- **Delegate with care.**

  - Phrase your request respectfully.

  - Let people know why the task is necessary.

  - Let them know why you've asked them.

  - Ask them how they think the task should be performed.

  - Ask them if they have any questions.

  - Ask them what kind of help they'll need.

  - Thank them in advance.

  - If you have time, offer assistance.

Summary cont.

- ### Give feedback carefully.

    - Let them know in advance you'll be giving them feedback.

    - Gather all the facts first.

    - Comment on both good and bad behaviors.

    - Don't get personal.

    - Don't overdo it.

    - Consider the time and place.

    - Choose your words carefully.

    - Keep it constructive and productive.

    - Ask them what they think they need to do.

    - Adapt your leadership style appropriately to the different kinds of personalities you lead.

Notes

PLATFORM PIZZAZZ
The Secret to Successful Public Speaking
"From a man's mouth you can tell who he is."

The ability to motivate, educate and persuade people from the platform is the sign of a powerful leader. If you can capture and hold an audience's attention – even if you don't have much experience -- you can lead them to action.

For some, this ability comes naturally. For others it requires some work. Let's face it, getting up in front of a group can be scary! In fact, studies have shown that more people are afraid of public speaking than they are of their own death.

You really can't lead others unless you can speak to them and inspire them to act. Fortunately, anyone can learn to give an effective presentation. This chapter will show you how.

©1999 Scott Greenberg

17

SPEAKERS YOU ADMIRE

One of the best ways to learn about public speaking is to study the masters. Let's take a look at the speakers who have influenced you.

Answer the following questions:

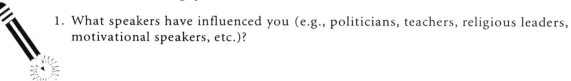

1. What speakers have influenced you (e.g., politicians, teachers, religious leaders, motivational speakers, etc.)?

2. What did these speakers do during their presentations that made them special?

3. How were these speakers similar to each other? How were they different?

4. What do you think had greater impact on you, their message or their speaking style? Could anyone else have given the same speech with equal impact?

Chances are these speakers combined a great speech with a powerful style. To effectively reach your audience, you need both.

WRITING A GREAT SPEECH

Although good speakers can make you think they're just saying what's on their mind, this is rarely the case. More often an effective presentation has been meticulously organized, prepared and practiced. When writing a speech, most speakers will break down their presentation into an INTRO, BODY and a CONCLUSION.

INTRO

Your objective with the beginning of your speech is to win your audience's attention and respect. This is where you'll make a first impression. Give them a reason to listen. Consider opening your speech with a story, a sure-fire joke or a quote. Find a way to grab 'em. You may even want to ask a question that the rest of your speech will answer. Then share the main idea of your speech which you will support with the rest of your presentation.

BODY

This is where you will support your main idea with sub-points. Your points can be made with statistics, stories and explanations -- anything that is interesting and backs up your main idea.

CONCLUSION

This is where you will summarize and repeat your main idea, and leave your audience with a call to action. Give them something to do. Then end with something powerful so your speech will make a lasting impression.

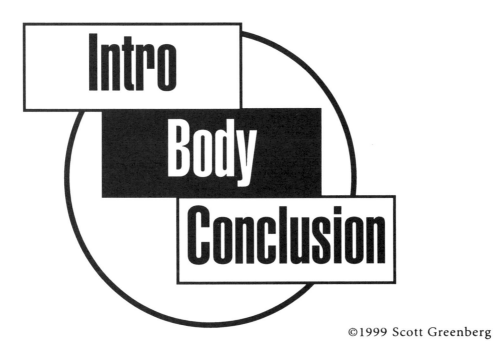

CREATING AN OUTLINE

Think of a topic for a speech you would give. Fill out the form below to outline this speech:

INTRO

Opening Line: _____

Story, Joke, Quote: _____

Key Idea: _____

Transitional Sentence to Body : _____

BODY

Sub-Point One:_____

1. _____

2. _____

3. _____

Sub-Point Two:_____

1. _____

2. _____

3. _____

Sub-Point Three: _____

1. _____

2. _____

3. _____

CONCLUSION

Key Idea: _____

Action You Want Audience To Take: _____

SO WHAT DO I SAY?

An outline can help you structure the speech, but it doesn't tell you what you should actually say to your audience. Only you can make that decision. Here are tips to help you develop your material:

Tell your stories.

Nothing interests audiences more than stories. The books of most religions are filled with stories that teach, inspire and sometimes even entertain us. Brainstorm everything that has ever happened to you that makes you unique. Then choose the stories that support the points you make in your speech. You may think you haven't done much, but if you really look back on your life, you will find stories -- small or big -- that are worth telling. If an experience had an impact on you, you can use it to impact an audience.

Tell others' stories.

Perhaps someone you know has experienced something interesting that will help you make your point. Be sure to get their permission first, and don't use the story if they are already telling it.

Keep it original.

When audiences realize they've heard something before, they stop listening. They may also compare you to other people they've heard. Using someone else's material can cause too many problems. Instead, create original material that comes straight from your head and heart.

Be honest.

Audiences can see right through a dishonest speaker. Don't say you've done something if you haven't. Be sincere and genuine. If an audience sees that you're for real, they'll be much more open to your presentation.

Practice what you preach.

If you are encouraging people to act or behave in a certain way, it is important that you yourself act that way. Don't say one thing and do something else. No one likes a hypocrite, and they certainly don't believe one. If you have made mistakes in the past and want to share what you've learned from them, that's something different. Just make sure you talk the talk and walk the walk.

Embellish.

While your basic content should be true, feel free to add a detail or two to your stories to make them more entertaining. Don't change the overall nature of your stories, but if creating a small detail will enhance the humorous or dramatic impact of the piece, don't be afraid to go for it.

Become an expert on your subject.

Research your topic thoroughly. Audiences can tell whether or not you really know what you're talking about. The more you know, the more you'll have to say.

Solicit ideas from others.

Brainstorm ideas with people you know and trust. While you're all alone when you give the speech, no one said you need to be alone writing it. Get other people's input and feedback.

Try your ideas on others.

See how other people respond to your thoughts. Often another person can give you a different perspective and improve your work.

Practice, practice, practice.

Practice in front of parents, siblings, friends – even the dog! Practice in front of the mirror. Give your speech to anyone who will listen. Experienced speakers write some of their best material while actually giving speeches. Something spontaneously comes to mind, they try it and it works. Speak as often as you can and your material will begin to evolve on its own.

SO HOW DO I SAY IT?

You may have written the best speech in the world, but if you can't deliver it well, it won't make much impact. The way you say things is actually more important than what you say. In fact, studies have shown that the way you use your voice in a speech has more than five times the impact of what you are saying. Non-verbal communication has eight times the impact! Your delivery is critical. And of course, so is your mental state.

Here are some tips to help in both areas:

Focus on your purpose.

You are there to share a message. That message is more important than having the audience like you. So instead of focusing on what they think of you, focus on whether or not they're hearing your message. Invariably when you do this, they'll like you more anyway.

Control your body language.

That means good posture, hands out of your pockets and comfortable movements. Audiences respect speakers who appear confident (whether they really are or aren't). Anything that suggests otherwise will lose you credibility.

Use your voice.

Try changing the volume or inflection of your voice to see how you can best make your point.

Make eye contact.

Look audience members right in the eye. That will make you seem in control of the situation.

Wait for silence.

Do not speak if many audience members are talking. You don't have to shush them or glare at them or plead with them to be quiet. Simply remain silent and wait. Generally they'll quiet down themselves. If it's only a few people occasionally whispering in a way that's really not distracting the audience, don't stop your presentation for them.

Arrive early to inspect the room where you'll be speaking.

Is the sound system good? Is there a door that closes loudly when people come in late? Is the lighting adequate? What do you notice that could affect how things go? Addressing these issues beforehand can help you avoid problems during your presentation.

Give your speech to everyone in the audience.

Many speakers have a tendency to focus on just one portion of the room. Be sure you're making eye contact and sharing your message with everyone.

Laugh at your mistakes.

Not only is it OK to make mistakes during the speech, but it actually allows you to appear more human. Audiences like that. What's most important is that you handle these mistakes well. Just smile and say "Whoops!" and go on. Show your audience that you're completely unfazed. That'll earn their respect. Speech problems are only as bad as you make them. And don't forget, they don't know what you're going to say. If you forget a section of the speech, they'll never know!

No matter what happens, just go on.

Audiences are more forgiving than you think. If you make a mistake or something goes wrong, compose yourself as quickly as possible and then proceed as if it never happened. Problems will always seem worse to you than to anyone else. Don't get down on yourself. A good speaker can recover from just about anything.

Leave the platform slowly and confidently.

You'll lose respect if you look like you're trying to make an escape. Be proud of what you just said.

Practice, practice, practice.

The more comfortable you are with the material, the more confident you'll be when you deliver it and the less likely you'll be to forget things.

Videotape and/or record your speeches.

Cameras and tape recorders don't lie. Watch and listen to your presentations to identify any bad habits. You may also discover something you do well.

Remember, the stakes aren't that high.

You really don't have much to lose when giving a speech. People are not judging or evaluating you as much as it may seem. They're just sitting there, just like you do when you're in the audience, taking in your speech. If your presentation is good, they'll remember it. If not, they'll forget all about it.

SPEECH ASSESSMENT

Use the chart below to gauge how you need to improve as a speaker. Then, practice giving a speech (perhaps on a topic you're already familiar with) to someone else and have them use the chart on the next page to evaluate your performance.

SELF ASSESSMENT

	Excellent	OK	Needs Improvement	Comments
CONTENT				
Intro	☐	☐	☐	
Establishing Main Idea	☐	☐	☐	
Transitions	☐	☐	☐	
Sub-points	☐	☐	☐	
Stories	☐	☐	☐	
Examples	☐	☐	☐	
Sincerity	☐	☐	☐	
Humor	☐	☐	☐	
Conclusion	☐	☐	☐	
Organization	☐	☐	☐	
SPEAKING STYLE				
Eye Contact	☐	☐	☐	
Posture	☐	☐	☐	
Gesturing	☐	☐	☐	
Pacing	☐	☐	☐	
Confidence	☐	☐	☐	
Facial Expressions	☐	☐	☐	
Volume	☐	☐	☐	
Voice Inflection	☐	☐	☐	
Handling of Mistakes	☐	☐	☐	
Handling of Distractions	☐	☐	☐	

OBSERVER ASSESSMENT

	Excellent	OK	Needs Improvement	Comments
CONTENT				
Intro	☐	☐	☐	
Establishing				
Main Idea	☐	☐	☐	
Transitions	☐	☐	☐	
Sub-points	☐	☐	☐	
Stories	☐	☐	☐	
Examples	☐	☐	☐	
Sincerity	☐	☐	☐	
Humor	☐	☐	☐	
Conclusion	☐	☐	☐	
Organization	☐	☐	☐	
SPEAKING STYLE				
Eye Contact	☐	☐	☐	
Posture	☐	☐	☐	
Gesturing	☐	☐	☐	
Pacing	☐	☐	☐	
Confidence	☐	☐	☐	
Facial Expressions	☐	☐	☐	
Volume	☐	☐	☐	
Voice Inflection	☐	☐	☐	
Handling of Mistakes	☐	☐	☐	
Handling of Distractions	☐	☐	☐	

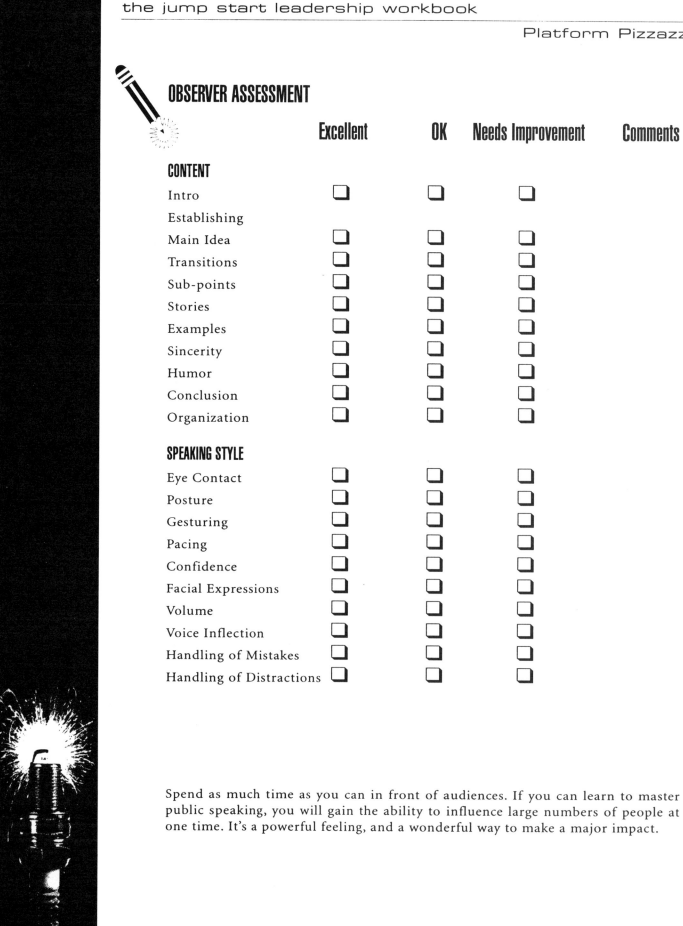

Spend as much time as you can in front of audiences. If you can learn to master public speaking, you will gain the ability to influence large numbers of people at one time. It's a powerful feeling, and a wonderful way to make a major impact.

SUMMARY

· Learn from speakers you admire.

· Begin writing your speech with an outline.

· INTRO: Open with a story, a sure-fire joke or a quote that will grab 'em.

· BODY: Support your main idea with sub-points.

· CONCLUSION: Summarize and repeat your main idea, and leave your audience with a call to action.

· Take time developing your material.

· Tell your stories.

· Tell others' stories.

· Keep it original.

· Be honest.

· Practice what you preach.

· Embellish.

· Become an expert on your subject.

· Solicit ideas from others.

· Try your ideas on others.

· Practice, practice, practice.

SUMMARY cont.

- What you say is not as important as how you say it.

- Spend time working on your speaking style.

  - Focus on your purpose.

  - Control your body language.

  - Use your voice.

  - Make eye contact.

  - Wait for silence.

  - Arrive early to inspect the room where you'll be speaking.

  - Give your speech to everyone in the audience.

  - Laugh at your mistakes.

  - No matter what happens, just go on.

  - Leave the platform slowly and confidently.

  - Practice, practice, practice.

  - Videotape and/or record your speeches.

  - Remember, the stakes aren't that high.

RUNNING MEETINGS
GETTING MAXIMUM RESULTS IN MINIMAL TIME

"To meet, or not to meet. That is the question."

Millions of meetings take place every day around the world. A third of these meetings are considered unnecessary by the people who attend them. But even the meetings that are necessary are often problematic. Ask most people how they feel about attending a meeting and they usually won't have pleasant things to say.

As a leader you will no doubt have to plan, attend and lead meetings. Fortunately, the process does not have to be painful. In fact, it can actually be quite productive. You just have to use the right techniques. This chapter will offer ideas for making your meetings more effective so you get more out of the time you share with your group.

IDENTIFYING COMMON PROBLEMS WITH MEETINGS

Let's begin by identifying the things that bother you about the meetings you attend. Think about all the clubs, committees and organizations you're a part of. Consider what your meeting time is like.

What are the most common problems with the meetings you attend?

1. _____
2. _____
3. _____
4. _____
5. _____
6. _____
7. _____
8. _____
9. _____
10. _____

11. _____
12. _____
13. _____
14. _____
15. _____
16. _____
17. _____
18. _____
19. _____
20. _____

Chances are these problems are not unique to the groups you're a part of. The fact is, it's just plain difficult to get a bunch of people together in one room to work together -- whether you're a student, teacher or corporate executive. Understanding the problems that plague your meetings will give you a place to start. From there, you can begin to make positive changes. As you read through this chapter, keep these issues in mind and see if you can pick up some ideas on how to resolve them.

When Are Meetings Necessary?

Answer: When there is information to be exchanged or decisions to be made that require people to be physically present. Often there are other ways to accomplish your objective without taking the time to hold a formal meeting. Alternatives include:

Phone calls	Memos
Mail	Postings in Public Areas
e-mail	Informal Conversations

If none of these alternatives will do the trick, then you probably have to have a meeting. Holding meetings only when necessary will add value to them and encourage better attitudes and greater participation. It will also respect people's valuable time.

TIPS TO MAKE YOUR MEETINGS EFFECTIVE

Most meetings are problematic because they are too loosely run. The person in charge of the meeting is afraid to be perceived as a control freak, and opts to be overly tolerant. However, if you are leading the meeting, it is in the group's best interest for you to take control. Remind them that you are doing so not because you love being in charge, but to help accomplish the objective of the meeting.

Here are some specific things you can do to get the most out of your meeting time.

Make sure the meeting has a clear purpose.

People need to know why they are there and what they are expected to accomplish. This will give them a greater interest in making the meeting work.

Establish agreements.

These are the rules everyone in the meeting will agree to in order to make the meeting run more smoothly. When you enforce one of these rules, remind them that it is their agreed-upon policy you're enforcing.

Ask group members for their suggestions and solutions to common problems, or for other problems that may come up.

Find out how they would like to handle meeting dilemmas, with a full understanding that you intend to enforce their policies.

Keep your meetings small.

The more people you have, the higher the chance of distractions, arguments, disagreements and grandstanding. If the meeting is smaller, more people have a chance to be heard and the easier it is to make decisions.

Ask only those people necessary for the meeting to come.

Few people like to attend meetings that really don't require them to be there. Don't waste anyone's time.

The larger the group, the more formal you should be.

It's easier to be more casual and relaxed when only a few people are present. However, as the number of participants increases, so does the number of problems. Enforce policies more strictly as the group size grows.

Start meetings on time.

Do this out of respect to those who make an effort to be on time, and as a message to those who come late.

Prepare an agenda before the meeting.

Then ask if anything else needs to be added. This will keep your time organized.

Assign appropriate time limits for each agenda item.

This will help you run on time and ensure there will be adequate time to address each item. Be sure to leave extra time for issues that may require more discussion.

Make every meeting meaningful.

Don't have a meeting if it doesn't serve an important purpose.

Prepare.

Do plenty of work in advance. This will keep your meeting organized and help you win the respect of those who attend. If they see you take the meeting seriously, they will be more likely to as well.

Be sensitive to the mood of the group.

Don't force things. If the group is losing energy, take a break or change the agenda appropriately. If they're distracted by something significant, address this and handle it accordingly.

Note common distractions.

Then find ways to prevent these distractions for future meetings.

What kinds of distractions come up during the meetings you attend? How might you address these distractions?

Meeting Distractions	Solutions
1. _____	_____
2. _____	_____
3. _____	_____
4. _____	_____
5. _____	_____

You will find additional solutions in the TROUBLESHOOTING GUIDE later in this chapter.

MEETING ROLES

One idea for preventing problems in a meeting is to assign people to specific meeting roles. These people focus less on what is discussed in the meeting and more on how it is discussed. They don't necessarily lead the group; they lead the meeting. The two main roles are the moderator and the recorder.

THE MODERATOR

This person facilitates discussion and runs the meeting. The moderator does not necessarily have to be the leader of the group (such as a president). It can be anyone willing to take charge of the meeting. This person's key purpose is to move the group through their agenda in the most productive manner. The moderator's responsibilities include:

· Keeping the group focused on the agenda.

· Remaining objective.

· Encouraging everyone to participate.

· Suggesting how to improve the meeting process.

· Maintaining order.

· Making sure everyone sticks to their group agreements.

· Making sure the meeting runs on time.

· Keeping the group's energy up.

· Making sure the recorder is keeping up.

· Addressing any issues that affect the meeting.

©1999 Scott Greenberg

THE RECORDER

This person will take notes on what is discussed for everyone to read during the meeting. This may mean writing on an overhead projector, or more commonly, on white butcher paper taped to the wall or on an easel. (Creating posters allows the record to be permanent and moveable. It will also allow you to display several records at once.) While a secretary may take notes to create an official record of the meeting, the recorder will create a visual record for everyone to focus on during the meeting. The recorder's responsibilities include:

· Using the words of group members.

· Remaining objective.

· Abbreviating and using symbols to save time.

· Writing in alternating colors to make each idea distinct.

The roles of the moderator and recorder can and should be changed to meet the needs of the group. For example, in an informal setting, the facilitator and recorder can be the same person. Or you may decide it's unnecessary for the recorder to use alternating colors. Do whatever works for your group.

©1999 Scott Greenberg

CREATING AN AGENDA

Set your meeting up for success by planning an agenda. Taking time to do this will help you clarify the purpose and goals for the meeting and what items must be addressed to achieve these goals. Below is an example of an agenda that many groups use to plan their meetings. On the following page you will find a blank form you can use for your own meetings. Remember, you can adapt it to meet your needs.

AGENDA FORM

DATE: <u>March 14, 1999</u>   TIME: <u>10:00 AM - 11:00 AM</u>

GOALS FOR MEETING:

- Update group on current activities
- Generate list of community service projects
- Decide where to have our retreat
- Decide on agenda for next meeting

ITEMS	WHO WILL LEAD DISCUSSION	TIME LIMIT
1. Roll Call	Secretary	5 minutes
2. Revue and Update Agenda	Moderator	3 minutes
3. Announcements	President	3 minutes
	Vice-Presidents	3 minutes
	Treasurer	3 minutes
	Mr. Robinson	3 minutes
4. Brainstorm community service projects	Moderator	10 minutes
5. Choose location for next retreat	Moderator	10 minutes
6.		
7.		
8.		
9. Brainstorm agenda items for the next meeting	Moderator	5 minutes
10. Review action to be taken	Moderator	2 minutes

AGENDA FORM

DATE:_____   TIME:_____

GOALS FOR MEETING:

•

•

•

•

ITEMS	WHO WILL LEAD DISCUSSION	TIME LIMIT
1. _____		
2. _____		
3. _____		
4. _____		
5. _____		
6. _____		
7. _____		
8. _____		
9. _____		
10. _____		

EFFECTIVE SEATING & ROOM ARRANGEMENT

Sometimes something as subtle as the seating and room arrangement can have a great impact on your meeting.

Here are some suggestions to make the room work for you:

Arrange the room so the door is in the back.

This will allow latecomers to arriving without distracting the group.

Silence the door.

If your door bangs shut or makes any kind of distracting noise, do something to fix it.

Hang a sign outside the room that says "Meeting in Progress."

People tend to be respectful of such signs and will be less likely to disturb you.

Tidy up the room.

If it looks sloppy, people will be less respectful during the meeting. Set up the room like you mean business.

Have audio visual tools ready.

This includes poster paper, markers, tape, overhead projectors, TV, VCR or anything else you need for the meeting.

Pre-cut and hang butcher paper.

This will make it easier for your recorder to get right to work once discussion starts.

Arrange furniture according to the meeting type.

Set up chairs in a circle if there will be a lot of personal sharing and discussion. Use a semi-circle when the group needs to focus on something such as a poster. Make tables or desks available when participants need to do a lot of writing (without changing the shape of the chair arrangement).

Put everyone at the same level.

Do not allow some to sit on chairs while others sit on the floor or lay on a couch. Everyone should be at approximately the same physical position.

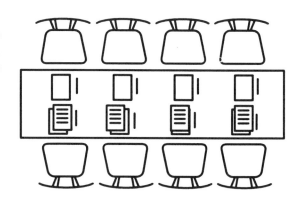

Pre-distribute handouts.

Have them on people's desks or chairs when they come into the room so you don't waste time passing them out during the meeting.

Set temperature to a comfortable level.

People get restless if it's too warm or too cold.

TROUBLESHOOTING GUIDE

Problem	Solution
Everything takes too long.	· Stick to your time limits. · Allot more time for meetings. · Put fewer items on the agenda. · Eliminate decisions or activities that don't necessarily need to occur during the meeting.
People regularly show up late.	· Start all meetings on time. · Offer food only for those who arrive before the meeting starts. · After meetings remind latecomers of group agreements. · Have the group create a tardy policy
Participants waiting to speak get tired of raising their hands.	· Number off everyone who would like to speak and then call on them in numerical order.
Recorder can't keep up with the group.	· Use multiple recorders.
Purpose for the meeting is unclear.	· Decide on purpose before meeting and communicate to all invited. · Repeat purpose at beginning of meeting.
Lots of side conversations.	· Remind group of agreements. · Change seating arrangement. · Have moderator stand near people who are talking. · Take a break. · Ask repeat offenders to leave.
Arguments/Disagreements	· Allow all sides to speak. · Record all points of view so they are not repeated.

Problem	Solution
Arguments/Disagreements cont.	· Postpone less important decisions to allow people to think, calm down and debate on their own. · Ask the main people from opposing sides to meet together away from the rest of the group to generate a solution they can co-present.
Some people dominate the meeting.	· Strictly enforce time limits for speaking. · Have moderator call on people with hands raised to give other people a chance to talk. · Have moderator ask if other people have something to share. · Ask dominant people to moderate rather than participate.
Time is taken to update latecomers.	· Keep a running record of main points of meetings that can be read at any time. · Wait until after meeting to update them.
Meeting feels disorganized.	· Set an agenda and prepare everything in advance. · Establish clear roles for meeting (i.e., moderator, recorder, timekeeper, etc.) · Keep an ongoing, visible record of your progress.
People from the outside disturb the meeting.	· Hang a sign outside that says "Meeting In Progress" · Hold meeting in a more private place. · Hold meeting during a more quiet time.

SUMMARY

- Identify the common problems with the meetings you attend.

- Make sure the meeting has a clear purpose.

- Establish agreements.

- Ask group members for suggestions and solutions to common problems, or for other problems that may come up.

- Keep your meetings small.

- Ask only those people necessary for the meeting to come.

- The larger the group, the more formal you should be.

- Start meetings on time.

- Prepare an agenda before the meeting.

- Assign appropriate time limits for each agenda item.

- Make every meeting meaningful.

- Prepare.

- Be sensitive to the mood of the group.

- Note common distractions.

- Use a Moderator and a Recorder to run your meetings.

- Use a standard format for your meeting agenda.

- Prepare your meeting room in the most effective set-up possible for your meeting.
  - Arrange the room so the door is in the back.
  - Silence the door.
  - Hang a sign outside that says "Meeting in Progress."
  - Tidy up the room.

Summary cont.

· Have audio visual tools ready.

· Pre-cut and hang butcher paper.

· Arrange furniture according to the meeting type.

· Put everyone at the same level.

· Pre-distribute handouts.

· Set temperature to a comfortable level.

· Find solutions to common meeting problems.
(See TROUBLESHOOTING GUIDE)

Notes

Surviving Conflict And Keeping the Peace

"We spend so much time convincing others we are right,
only because we fear we may be wrong."

Anytime people get together you can expect there to be some conflict. All of us have different needs, opinions and backgrounds. We all have our own perspective that influences what we say or do. If you get two or more people together, it's only a matter of time before these perspectives clash.

However, this isn't necessarily a bad thing. Our whole legislative system is based on organized debate. Through the process of exchanging different ideas, we are able to come up with the best solutions. Most sports are based on conflict. One side wants to send the ball in one direction, the other side in the opposite. What fun would a football game be if both teams wanted the ball to go into the same end zone? Indeed, conflict keeps life interesting.

It can also make things quite stressful. When two people want different things (or are fighting over the same thing) the situation can get ugly. Chances are there's someone in your life right now with whom you have bad feelings – a friend, teacher, parent, sibling, etc.

If you have problems resolving this conflict, you're not alone. The world's greatest minds offer advice to our leaders, yet still there is war all over the planet. Our courts are filled with business people, couples and everyday citizens who can't agree. Our parents fight, our teachers fight – even our pets fight!

It is an unfortunate reality that where there are people, there is conflict. While there is little you can do to escape it, there's a lot you can do to minimize it. In fact, most conflicts are actually quite avoidable or easily resolved. You just have to know the right techniques. And that's what this chapter is all about.

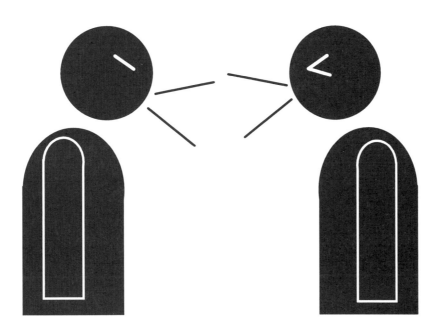

HOW DO YOU CONTRIBUTE TO CONFLICT?

Very rarely are we completely innocent in a fight. For there to be tension in a rope, it needs to be pulled in two different directions. If it were only being pulled on one end, there would be no tension.

 Similarly, it takes two people to fight. One person may be more at fault than another, but it's likely that everyone is adding fuel to the fire. With this in mind, identify what you do that may cause conflict.

Answer the following questions for yourself:

1. How do I judge and evaluate others?

2. How do I think other people judge and evaluate me?

3. Where does most of my conflict with others originate?

4. How do I usually deal with conflict?

5. What can I do differently to improve the way I manage conflict with others?

WHY BE RIGHT?

List all the advantages of being right in an argument:

- _____
- _____
- _____
- _____
- _____

Have any trouble? Many people do. Some people say it feels good to be right. Why? Does this earn you respect or admiration? Do you not earn respect and admiration when you admit you are wrong? Some people say being right will allow them to get their way. Why is your way so important? In most situations, how do you truly benefit from doing things your way and not someone else's?

After giving this issue some thought, most people agree there really is no significant advantage to being right. If you can give up your need to be right, you will suddenly find yourself in a powerful position. Most people get into fights and start arguing just for the sake of being right. They are terrified of what will happen if they are wrong. But think about it. If you are in a tug-of-war with someone, each pulling on the opposite side of a rope, and you let go, who is more powerful?

By letting go, you're the one who ended the tension. Disagreements are no different. If you can focus more on resolving the problem rather than on being right, you will earn people's respect and admiration and find your relationships to be a lot less stressful. Sure it feels good to be right. It feels better to resolve conflict.

PREVENTING CONFLICT

Techniques to avoid conflict before it arises

The best way to deal with conflict is to prevent it from happening in the first place. Taking the time to use the following tools can save you from lots of headaches.

Agree on goals.

When you enter a new situation with someone (e.g., a team, a relationship, a club, etc.), it is important that you both want the same things. Otherwise, your conflicting ideas may lead to conflicting behaviors. If you have a new boyfriend or girlfriend and one of you wants a serious relationship while the other just wants to date casually, someone is going to get upset. If some members of a football team want to win the championship as a team while others just want to show off for themselves, there are going to be problems. Make sure that everyone wants the same thing.

Set and agree on rules.

Once everyone agrees on what they want, you should make some agreements about how to behave. Using the relationship example above, you might decide whether or not it is acceptable to date other people. A football team should come to a consensus on who should run the ball during a key play. We have laws set up to avoid conflicts and problems. Create your own rules and agreements to prevent any disagreements later on when there's a lot more to lose.

Stay committed to success.

Rather than focusing on being right or getting what you want, always look at your common goals. If you remain committed to achieving these goals, you will rise above the petty arguments and ego problems that often create bad feelings.

Agree to communicate.

Most conflict comes from people communicating poorly or not at all. Many people keep their feelings inside, letting them build and come out in all sorts of unhealthy ways (e.g., lies, insults, violence, etc.). Chances are the majority of the conflicts you've resolved with people during your life have been handled by talking things out. If you agree to always communicate, you're more likely to handle your differences before they get out of hand.

Agree that it's OK to have conflict.

Make this agreement before it comes up. Many people are quite fearful of conflict, believing that even the slightest amount of tension can threaten their relationships. Remind each other that conflict is a natural part of growing together and that so long as you handle it in a healthy way, there's nothing to be afraid of.

Identify potential sources of conflict before they occur.

If you examine the situations you are in, you can anticipate potential problems. This will allow you to prevent these problems and/or resolve them early. Again, the idea is that you handle conflict before emotions run high.

Let's practice this. What potential conflicts could come up in the following situations? How might you prevent this conflict?

1. Your club or organization has a new advisor.

Potential conflicts:

How to prevent:

2. Two people of different religions get married.

Potential conflicts:

How to prevent:

3. You and a friend decide to take a vacation together.

Potential conflicts:

How to prevent:

4. You get a fancy new car.

Potential conflicts:

How to prevent:

There could be many answers to these questions. The idea is that you should ask these questions early so you can handle any conflicts in advance.

CONFLICT INTERVENTIONS

Techniques to manage conflict after it arises

Even if you do everything you can to prevent it, conflict can still come up. Here are some powerful techniques to take control of these problems and resolve them in the most painless way possible.

Find the right time for discussion.

Don't try to work through a problem when you don't have time to talk or when you're boiling over with anger. Wait until everyone has had a chance to calm down and there is enough time to talk.

Find the right place for discussion.

Find some place quiet, private and neutral.

Consider the best process of discussion.

Before launching into an argument, consider how best to communicate. Are you both going to start screaming? Will each person take turns? Talk about how you want to talk. This formal step will help maintain order and prevent the discussion from becoming chaotic.

Find a win/win scenario.

Look for solutions that will please everyone. While this can come from compromising, it can also come from creativity. Perhaps there is a solution neither of you have thought of that will allow both of you to get your way. For example, one person wants to spend a vacation skiing in Colorado, but the other wants the excitement of a Las Vegas casino. Maybe they can go to Lake Tahoe where there are both slopes and slots. Keep your mind open and be creative.

Attack the problem, not the person.

It's easy to take our disagreements and turn them into personal issues. Often relatively minor problems become huge, tearful fights because people start name-calling and criticizing personalities. Letting your conflicts get personal will only hurt people's feelings and increase tension.

If appropriate, solicit feedback from others before confrontation.

Sometimes we allow ourselves to get angry with someone because of our perceptions. Often an objective third party such as a friend or parent can help you understand other perspectives. If you can do it without violating someone's trust, consider sharing your feelings with someone not involved in the conflict and ask for their thoughts. Maybe they can point a few things out that will increase your understanding of the situation before you have a confrontation.

Listen without judgement or evaluation.

If someone is sharing their feelings with you and in you're mind your thinking "This is a bunch of baloney!," then you're not giving the person your full attention. Keep an open mind and really try to listen.

Don't prepare your next response when you should be listening.

Sometimes it feels good to come back with a clever comment, but rarely does that resolve the conflict. Stop yourself from preparing your response and just listen.

Take a moment to think about what the person has said, then repeat it.

Make sure they feel you understand them. Often people don't want you to apologize or change your behavior. They just want you to listen and understand their feelings. You've probably felt this way yourself before. When someone disagrees with you, don't be so quick to respond with your side of things. Instead, let them know that you understand their feelings (and make sure that you do).

Focus on one conflict at a time.

Just because one problem has come up doesn't mean it's time to open the flood gates and start arguing about every problem there is. Remain focused on the problem at hand.

Avoid tangents.

Keep your attention on resolving the current problem.

Avoid pointing out hypocrisy.

If someone points out a behavior of yours they don't like, it won't help for you to do the same. We all have different needs. Just ask yourself what can be done to resolve the current problem.

Avoid broad criticisms such as "You always..." or "You never..."

No one responds well to these sweeping generalizations, and usually they can prove you wrong.

Avoid words such "but" or "however."

You can say the most wonderful thing in the world about a person, but if you follow it up with "but" or "however," it completely invalidates the comment. Just say "and," or end the sentence and begin your next comment. For example, "For the last two weeks you've been great. This week there are some problems that we need to talk about."

Keep the volume down and be polite.

Yelling has a way of intensifying your emotions and raising the heat of a discussion. If you can control your emotions, you're more likely to keep a clear head and resolve the problem.

> TIP: If the other person is starting to yell, lower your voice. That has a way making them aware of how they're behaving, and it prevents you from feeling like you're being controlled in the discussion.

Monitor the progress of the discussion.

Every few minutes ask yourself (or even the other person) if you're actually making progress or just beating a dead horse. If you're not getting anywhere, figure out why and make the appropriate changes in the way you're communicating.

Be reasonable, sensitive and cooperative, but don't sacrifice your own feelings.

Rarely is it entirely your fault. If you have some bad feelings, take them seriously. Don't apologize if later on you're going to feel the same way and bring the subject up again. If you feel bad, you have a right to have that feeling addressed. If you don't deal with it, it won't go away.

Review discussion for next time.

Take a moment to talk about how well you worked through this problem so you can learn how to better resolve future conflicts.

RESOLVING CURRENT CONFLICTS

Often you can better enable yourself to resolve conflicts by writing them down and then brainstorming ways to address them. This will help you organize your thoughts. In the left side of chart below, list four current conflicts that trouble you. On the right side, list steps you might take to resolve these conflicts.

Current Conflicts In Your Life	Steps to Resolve These Conflicts
Example: My sister and I both need the car at the same time.	· See if one of us can reschedule our plans · See if one of us can get someone else to drive. · See if there's a way for one of us to drive the other or share the car. · Trade this car use for another time. · Agree to flip a coin!
1.	
2.	
3.	
4.	
5.	

Learning to resolve conflict effectively can be one of the most powerful skills a person can have. The techniques discussed here are proven to work. Incorporate them into your life and your relationships and you will enjoy more harmony than you can imagine.

SUMMARY

- Identify your habits that contribute to creating conflict.

- There is no advantage to being right.

- Prevent conflict before it arises.

  - Agree on goals.

  - Set and agree on rules.

  - Stay committed to success.

  - Agree to communicate.

  - Agree that it's OK to have conflict.

  - Identify potential sources of conflict before they occur.

- Use interventions to manage conflict when it arises.

  - Find the right time for discussion.

  - Find the right place for discussion. Consider the best process of discussion.

  - Find a win/win scenario.

  - Attack the problem, not the person.

  - If appropriate, solicit feedback from others before confrontation.

  - Listen without judgement or evaluation.

  - Don't prepare your next response when you should be listening.

  - Take a moment to think about what the person has said, then repeat it. Make sure they feel you understand them.

  - Focus on one conflict at a time.

SUMMARY cont.

- Avoid tangents.

- Avoid pointing out hypocrisy.

- Avoid broad criticisms such as "You always…" or "You never…"

- Avoid words such "but" or "however."

- Keep the volume down and be polite.

- Monitor the progress of the discussion.

- Be reasonable, sensitive and cooperative, but don't sacrifice your own feelings.

- Review discussion for next time.

- Write down conflicts and brainstorm on paper solutions to address them.

Notes

POWER NETWORKING

"It's not what you know, it's who you know. And who you know is less important than who knows you."

The most important resource a leader can have is relationships. All of us have different talents, abilities and connections. When we unite and share these elements with others, everyone is more powerful. It's nice to have people you can call on for favors. It also feels good when you can help someone else. As a leader, your ability to network and call upon your connections can be a tremendous advantage when you're trying to get something done.

Some people are uncomfortable with networking. They're afraid they're "using" people. However, the best networkers are those who offer as many favors as they solicit. We all need other people in our lives. Networking is about creating relationships that benefit everyone. There's no reason why this can't be done in an honest, genuine manner.

The ability to create and maintain these relationships is an acquired skill. This chapter will offer ideas for meeting powerful people and creating your network.

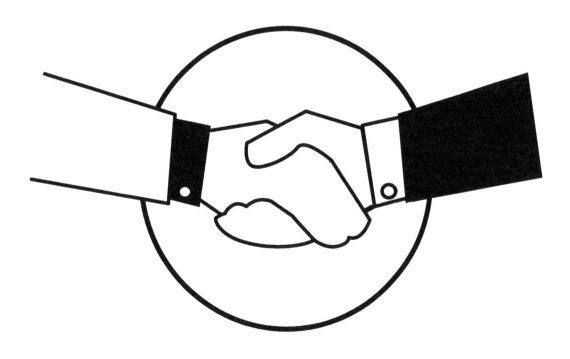

©1999 Scott Greenberg

YOUR CURRENT NETWORK

Think of yourself as the hub of a bicycle tire, connected to everyone you know. In the illustration below, fill your name in the center and at the end of each spoke, write down the names of the 25 people in your life who are most in a position to help you (e.g., teachers, coaches, family friends, employers – anyone you know who has power).

We will refer to these people as your top 25.

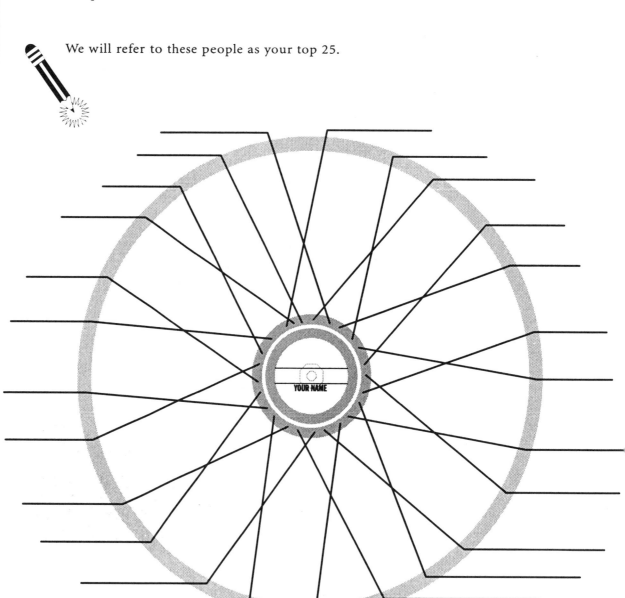

©1999 Scott Greenberg

YOUR EXPANDED NETWORK

Everyone who you're connected to is also the center of their own circles. If each one of them has 25 connections, you're already connected (directly or indirectly) to 650 people! Most of these people know a lot more than 25 other people, making your network even bigger.

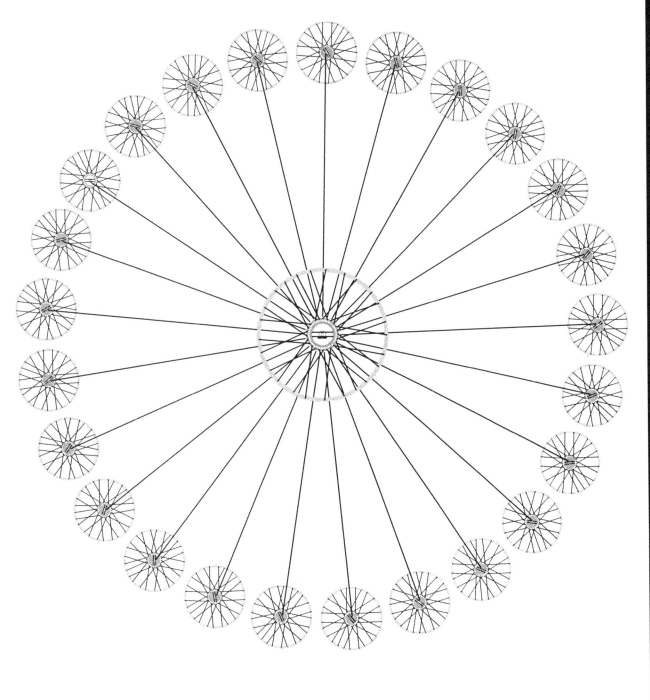

On the left side of the chart below, list a few people from your top 25. On the right side, list someone powerful they know. Take some time to find out who that might be. You'll be surprised.

Your Connection	Their Connection

Often your top 25 will be happy to introduce you to their connections or speak on your behalf to them. But don't wait for them to offer to do this. Part of networking is being able to ask for the introduction. Sometimes it may not be appropriate, but more often they'll be happy to help you out.

MAKING NEW CONNECTIONS

Now it's time to put on the charm and start making new connections. Here's how:

Get out and meet people.

Go to parties, conferences, classes, meetings, clubs, organizations – anywhere people get together. Exposing yourself to new groups will offer you new relationships. Go to settings where you'll find the kind of people you want to meet.

Where can you go to meet new people?

_____

_____

_____

_____

_____

Find people who get other people's attention.

In any setting where people are talking, there always seems to be certain people whose presence commands attention. Look for small circles of people surrounding and listening to one person. This type of person is generally pretty powerful and worth getting to know.

Never assume someone isn't worth your time.

Most often our first impression of people is misleading. You have no idea who can help you, who you can help, or who might turn out to be a great friend.

Don't be afraid to introduce yourself.

If you wait too long to approach someone, you'll psyche yourself out of doing it. If you have an opportunity to meet someone, move right in. Can't think of anything to say? How about "Hi, I'm…", telling them your name and shaking their hand. The rest will come out naturally. Do it with comfort and confidence and it'll put the other person at ease. It's really that easy.

Listen more than you talk.

No one likes to listen to others talk about themselves. They prefer when you take a genuine interest in who they are. Use this time to get to know them, rather than asking for favors.

Listen for what people need and think of ways to help them.

Spend time finding ways to help the people you meet and connect them to others you know can help them. That will win you considerably more favor than anything else you do. When you actively try to help someone, they will remember it and instinctively brainstorm ways they can help you. Assisting others also just plain feels good.

Always ask for a business card.

Even if you don't see how you may be able to work with this person in the future, you never know. You also don't know who they know who can help you. File their card away for future reference. If they don't have a business card, write down their contact information somewhere else.

Write on the back of the business cards you collect.

Getting someone's card won't help you if you forget who they are or what you discussed. After meeting someone and getting their card, take a moment to make notes on the back of the card of what you discussed, jokes you shared and any other details that will make the person stand out.

Make reference to these details when contacting the people you meet.

Repeat the joke you shared, or refer to something significant that came up. If these particulars help you remember the person, they'll help the person remember you as well.

Get your own business cards.

Even if you don't have a job, having business cards with your phone number makes it easier for people to contact you. But don't wait for someone to call you. The purpose of your business card is to allow you to get someone else's card and follow up with them.

©1999 Scott Greenberg

Follow up.

After you meet someone new, contact them as soon as possible. If you promised to call, then call. You can also send a quick e-mail. The best approach is to send a short note in the mail telling the person how much you enjoyed meeting them. Be sure to personalize the note by making reference to one of the particulars you noted on the back of their business card.

Don't be afraid to follow up.

Often you meet someone and really connect with them, but then the next day you feel uncomfortable calling. Ignore that feeling and call anyway. Whatever connected you when you met will still be there.

Write letters to people you want to meet.

Often they will respond.

Seek mentors.

Ask powerful people to be your mentor. They'll be honored. Tell them you just want to meet for half an hour every three months — not to ask for favors, but just to ask questions and get ideas. Often they'll offer to help you out anyway. You'd be surprised how many important, influential people would agree to meet with you.

Be genuine.

Networking is not about using people. It's about cultivating true, caring relationships that benefit everyone. Beware of manipulating people, being dishonest or taking advantage. It doesn't take long to develop a bad reputation. The more honest you can be, the more people will want your company, and the more they'll be willing to help.

MAINTAINING YOUR CONNECTIONS

Once you meet people, you need to maintain your relationship with them. Here are some ideas for keeping these people in your life.

Create a system for keeping track of everyone you know.

This might mean a database, a Rolodex or some other system to make sure you don't forget about anyone.

Clip newspaper and magazine articles for people.

If you find a story that is relevant to someone's life, cut it out and send it to them. They'll really appreciate the thought.

Keep your eyes open for opportunities for people you know.

Refer them for jobs or anything else that helps their life. The favor will mean the world to them.

Acknowledge your contacts' birthdays.

Find out when they are and send them a card.

Acknowledge your contacts' achievements.

Send them a congratulations card if they accomplish something significant. Most people get less kudos than you think, and appreciate when someone takes the time to acknowledge them.

Be honest and direct.

If you're calling for a favor, be honest about that. Don't pretend your call is social and then slip in that you need something. People are busy and will appreciate you being straight with them. Just say, "Hi, I need a favor."

Respect your contacts' time and space.

Again, they might be quite busy. Don't waste their time. Be a person with whom it's easy to have a relationship. Don't be a pest.

Respect their limitations.

Sometimes your contacts can't help you. Respect that and thank them anyway.

Obey the 30-day rule for your top 25.

Make sure that you never go 30 days without contacting everyone on your top 25 list. That'll prevent them from forgetting about you. This doesn't mean necessarily having a meeting. A phone call, fax, e-mail, letter or informal personal visit will be just as effective.

the jump start leadership workbook

Power Networking

CONTACT SHEETS

Create a contact sheet for each member of your top 25 to keep track of your conversations. That will help you remember when you last communicated and what was discussed. You may wish to use something similar to the chart below:

CONTACT NAME:		
Date	What Was Discussed	Date for Next Call

©1999 Scott Greenberg

63

SUMMARY

· **Identify your top 25 connections.**

· **Find out who your top 25 connections know.**

· **Make new connections.**

> · Get out and meet people.
>
> · Find people who get other people's attention.
>
> · Never assume someone isn't worth your time.
>
> · Don't be afraid to introduce yourself.
>
> · Listen more than you talk.
>
> · Listen for what people need and think of ways to help them.
>
> · Always ask for a business card.
>
> · Write down the details of your conversations on the back of the business cards you collect.
>
> · Make reference to some of these details when contacting the people you meet.
>
> · Get your own business cards.
>
> · Follow up.
>
> · Don't be afraid to follow up.
>
> · Write letters to people you want to meet.
>
> · Seek mentors.
>
> · Be genuine.

SUMMARY cont.

· Maintain your connections.

- Clip newspaper and magazine articles for people.

- Keep your eyes open for opportunities for people you know.

- Acknowledge your contacts' birthdays.

- Acknowledge your contacts' achievements.

- Be honest and direct.

- Respect your contacts' time and space.

- Respect their limitations.

- Create a system for keeping track of everyone you know.

- Use contact information sheets to keep tract of your connections.

Notes

THE ADVENTURE AHEAD

You now have the knowledge you need to inspire, influence and mobilize others. It's very powerful. I urge you to put this power to good use. Don't abuse it. You could single handedly improve our world. I hope you'll choose to do so.

This workbook series is designed to jump start your career as a leader. To complete this journey, the burden is on you to do the work. Nothing you've read in these books will help you if you don't take action. Use the knowledge you have and apply what you've learned. You will get results.

Good luck on your adventure. May your path be smooth and the wind be at your back.

©1999 Scott Greenberg

If you have any questions, or would like further information on keynotes, leadership seminars, books or audio tapes by Scott Greenberg, call:

1-800-450-0432

Or check out our web site at:

www.scottgreenberg.com

©1999 Scott Greenberg